SHERLOCK HOLMES

THE RED DEATH

A. CONAN DOYLE

Adaptation:
A.-P. DUCHÂTEAU

Illustration:
G. CLAIR

RAVETTE BOOKS

Translated from the original story
La Sangsue Rouge
A. Conan Doyle – A. -P. Duchâteau – G Clair
© 1990 Claude Lefrancq Editeur

Rights gained from Yaffa Character Licensing

This edition first published by Ravette Books Limited 1992

Printed and bound for Ravette Books Limited,
3 Glenside Estate, Star Road, Partridge Green,
Horsham, West Sussex RH13 8RA
An Egmont Company
by Proost International Bookproduction, Belgium

ISBN: 1 85304 463 6

It was one of those evenings when my friend Sherlock Holmes seemed determined to live up to the image I have portrayed of him in my simple little stories...

It was the lazy sort of evening that I myself looked forward to – although Holmes invariably grew listless, depressed and irritable...

Oh. I beg of you, Watson! I'd be grateful if you could avoid using that odious little phrase 'And they lived happily ever after'!

Pardon? What...?

MR HOLMES! MR HOLMES!

You were staring at an article in 'The Times': Colonel Warburton has taken leave of his senses and killed his wife. You shook your head two or three times and then absent-mindedly looked at the picture of the young woman – and back at her husband again...

What is the matter, my dear Mrs Hudson?

There's a man... on the front door steps... he can hardly stand up... I think he's dying... he keeps repeating your name...

AARGH AARGH

Watson! This man is seriously ill... Call a doctor, quickly!

But... I AM a doctor!

Holmes! You must save me from THE RED DEATH!

Oh, why not? You only live once! . . . don't want to HIC go home. . . not yet anyway. . . I want ADVENTURE! . . .

I thought I was dreaming. The invisible coachman cracked his whip and the horse set off. . .

SHLAAK

Hm! The same thing happened to me! Did he take you far, Lord Brewster?

I have no idea! I just dozed off! . . . But the next thing I knew . . .

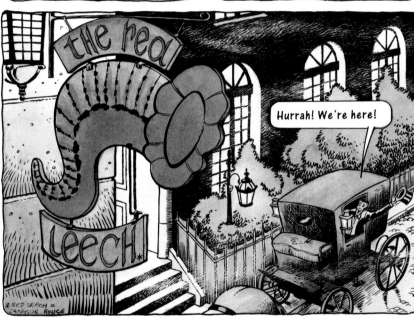

the red LEECH*

Hurrah! We're here!

HOUPS!

9A)

?

There seemed to be a seat waiting for me at one of the gaming tables. . . I eased myself into it!

And then. . . oh! . . . the HORROR! the RUIN!

9B)

In the space of one depraved evening, I signed away my fortune and my honour.

I lost everything we own — I even had to sign an acknowledgement of my debts . . . in my own blood!

My love! There's the money I inherited! Take it all! It's YOURS!

No, Violet! No! I couldn't do a thing like that!

Now you know everything, Mr Holmes! They . . They have condemned me to death! When the cab with the invisible coachman stopped outside the house, it meant one thing. . my EXECUTION!

. . . and you took me for your executioner!

This case is already a tricky one! You see how they managed to bring me here in the hope that we would kill one another!

But . . . I don't follow you!

Tell me, do you have in your employ a man who wears spectacles and looks a little like that actor. . .

Oh. yes! That's Dale, our butler! He came to work for us a few weeks ago!

He had an excellent reference from . . . who was it now? . . .

. . . May I see the letter, Lady Brewster?

I'll go and get it. . .

I hereby declare that Mr Dale has been a trustworthy and loyal servant. Professor Moriarty

G·CLAIR · A.P. DUCHATEAU ·

Later on, back at Baker Street

Moriarty alive! Back from the dead?! It's impossible Holmes! You managed to escape with your life at the Falls of Reichenbach, but Moriarty......

Moriarty is the criminal genius of all time! He is capable of anything!...

That unemployed actor, Dale - short-sighted fellow, specialised in provincial tours!...

How did you guess that, Holmes?

How many more times, Watson? I never guess! A reddish mark near his nose told me that Dale usually wore glasses... and some traces of powder and eye shadow suggested to me that he had been made to play the part of a butler...

.. But his skin was puckered as if he often used make up! I then thought he might be an actor - not a very good one - probably doing provincial towns. At all events. Moriarty probably ordered him... to find work in Lord Brewster's household...

The poor man must have betrayed the criminal organisation of the Red Leech, which then took its cruel revenge _ and he only came to me after he saw the advertisement in the 'Strand'.

We had to take him off to hospital, Holmes! He's not in his right mind any more!...

I was looking forward to a quiet, relaxed evening at home, Watson, but I'm afraid we still have work to do! Put your coat on, and make sure you bring a firearm with you!

11A

11B

You went to all the trouble of taking Dale to hospital; how, then, did he manage to get out and come here dressed as me?

Search me, Holmes!...

...but you know, all the time he was delirious, I kept on thinking of that viper Moriarty. Do you think he could have anything to do with it?

If the monster is still alive, I tremble to think what he is scheming!

I say! I say! What's going on here?

Carrington! Good evening! Not a pretty sight, I'm afraid! But tell me, what brings you to these parts?

It's Dale... Dale the butler!

Quite so! But perhaps you could answer my question!

Please don't think I'm interfering in your investigations. I just want to find those villains who ruined my friend Brewster!...

...When I got to the 'Red Leech', I spotted the cab and saw you running down towards the river!

Unfortunately, we got here too late! The poor wretch died a horrific death – I can't make it out at all!

We'd better let Inspector Lestrade know – he can arrange for the body to be taken away!

I'm relying on you, Carrington, to make sure your friends the Brewsters do not open their door to anyone tonight!

I'll go straight away! I'm a pretty good shot – amateur, you know – I'll stand on guard till morning if necessary!

That's a very brave man, Watson, but I'm afraid that the forces of evil won't be frightened off by a few revolvers! Let's go back to our cab!

Well, here we are but, as I expected, the red cab has vanished!

HOLMES! The gambling den.... the 'Red Leech'... It's all lit up!

14B

Let's go and have a look inside. Watson! Perhaps it'll be full of ghosts!

You don't believe that people can make themselves invisible, do you?

Well, you know, the American writer Edgar Allan Poe has published something about it, and over here the young novelist H. G. Wells is currently writing a book – called 'The Invisible Man'!

I don't like the look of this place one bit!

The gamblers are wearing masks!. . . but at least they're not invisible!

Excuse me, Sir!. . . I don't believe you're a member of the 'Red Leech' club. . .

SO HOP IT!

I know your face! Yes. . . you're Bonny the Bull! You were a fine boxer in your day, but unfortunately you took to the bottle. . .

HOLMES! THE BLOKE FROM SCOTLAND YARD! I'M GOING TO. . .!

Holmes! That man's as strong as an ox! Let me take over - there's a good chap - otherwise. . .

No! Let me play with him for a moment, Watson! It's all part of the investigation.

Well, Bonny! Still playing by the Queensbury Rules? Or don't you go in for that sort of thing anymore?

What's that got to do with you. . Ouch!. . Yeah! I. . .oof!. . . still fight clean!

That's all I wanted to know, my dear chap! Sorry to have to terminate this little interlude, but. . .

. . .I'm in a HURRY!

16A

This is serious gambling!

Don't be fooled by the elaborate masks, though! Behind each one lurks an aristocrat leading a double life - and a squalid, seedy life at that!. . .

16B

... In other words, Watson, they bet enormous sums of . . . QUIET! THIS IS THE INVISIBLE ONE!

I AM AMONGST YOU BUT YOU CANNOT SEE ME! GAMBLING IS AN IMMORAL BUSINESS!. . . I AM OPPOSED TO DIFFERENCES IN SOCIAL CLASS AND FAMILY FORTUNE! EVERYONE SHOULD HAVE AN EQUAL CHANCE!

Good gracious!

Carrington! Aren't you supposed to be at Brewster Lodge?

Yes, but I was curious. . . I just had to come. . . Did you hear?. . . That voice?. . .

Some evil genius who just disappears into thin air!

Not so fast, Watson! I think you'll find the invisible man is still here. . . I don't think he's gone far!. . .

VOUUUUOUUUf

Somebody's turned the lights off! Stay right by me, Watson! Don't go away!

By Jove! I can smell paraffin!. . .

But the terrified, panic-stricken gamblers ignore the advice, and take to their heels. Holmes and Watson are pushed and shoved and jostled.

. . . and then bundled to one side.

Anyone who slips is immediately trampled underfoot. . .

Later, when the police arrive, and the fire brigade comes to put out the fire. . .

ALIVE?

It's quite simple, my dear Watson! The man has been dressed in a striped vest to make him look like a skeleton! Help me get it off him!

The poor wretch! He's covered with red leeches positively sated with blood – just like Dale! Perhaps it's another servant!

No! This gentleman is a member of the aristocracy – those white hands have never done manual work! And you see the pale circle round this finger? Once upon a time, there used to be a very expensive ring here...!

Moriarty has thrown down the gauntlet, Watson!... The Red Death on our own doorstep!...

We'll try and save him, Holmes, but it may be too late! The poor man has lost just about every drop of blood in his body – blue or otherwise!

Do you think you could carry him into your room on your own?

Of course? He isn't very heavy! But where are you off to?

22A

Who knows? This well-trained horse might take me straight to his invisible master! But first, I'm going to go and see Lord and Lady Brewster!

What for?

You're quite right, Holmes! You always are!

I'm certain they'll be able to identify this poor man – I'm sure he moves in the same social circles as they do!

Giddy up, Blackie! Let's go!

How do you know he's called Blackie?

I don't my dear Watson! I just called him that OUT OF THE BLUE!

!?

22B

SCHLAAAK AAAARGH!

He's fallen off!... Better stop my horse before...

OH! OH!

He's got up again! There he goes!

24A

Which way did he go? He must have run off up this drive...

But... the place is DESERTED! And yet this is the only way he could have come!

24B

HA! HA! HA! HA! HA! HA! HA!

WE SHALL MEET AGAIN HOLMES! YOU THOUGHT YOU TRIUMPHED AT THE FALLS OF REICHENBACH! YOU WERE WRONG! REVENGE WILL BE MINE!

I don't believe it! I could have sworn... HE MUST BE HERE!

In... Invisible... with no b... body at all!...

It is most mysterious... I would be grateful, though, Lord Brewster... Carrington..., if you could identify the Red Death's latest victim...

Any time, Holmes!

Of course!

The two red cabs have vanished

We can go in mine, Holmes!

26A

Later, in Baker Street...

And how is our mystery invalid coming along?

Same as Dale. I'm afraid – delirium, fever...

Lord Brewster, Carrington! Do you know this man?

I'll say I do!

26B

What?

It's the Grand Duke!... Holmes! Watson! You must do everything you can to save this man's life!

Grand Duke?

May I introduce you to GRAND DUKE SERGEI ITCHKIN, one of the Tsar's most trusted associates! He's been in this country for several months on a diplomatic mission!

Do you mean to say that?...

I'm beginning to see, Lord Reginald, that this business of getting you to acknowledge your gambling debts is one of Moriarty's more sinister tricks!

Now, let me think... did you... er.. by any chance first meet Grand Duke Sergei Itchkin at the... er... 'Red Leech'?

I'm afraid so... and he was playing for high stakes – VERY HIGH INDEED!

Presumably he signed the acknowledgement of his debts with his own blood... and then had to default!

27A

How dreadful! If this got out, it would lead to a huge political scandal!

Yes, and the effect on diplomatic relations with Russia would be catastrophic!

Mrs Hudson! What's troubling you? Can I be of assistance?

Somebody else with red leeches arriving in a mysterious cab?

There are two gentlemen waiting to see you, sir... Two gentlemen... it's a confidential matter, you understand...

That's all right, Mrs Hudson! Show Mr Brown and Mr Smith in immediately!

How do you know those were their names?

Were you expecting these two gentlemen to visit us, Holmes?

Not in the least, Watson, but they wish our meeting to be confidential... moreover, Smith and Brown are the most commonly assumed names in such circumstances...

IN THE NAME OF HOLY RUSSIA! LET NO ONE MOVE!

!?

27B

One hour later, as I watched my friend, Sherlock Holmes, carefully remove the top of his sixth boiled egg...

Healthy appetite this morning, I see!...

What a remarkably astute observation, Watson!

You can't play the violin at this time! You'll wake up all the neighbours!

You know perfectly well, Watson, that it helps me to concentrate!

It might help you, but what about me?

Which is better? Me being able to concentrate or you NOT being able to concentrate?

How many times have I told you not to burst in like that without?...

That's all right. Watson! I'm sure they've got something very interesting to tell us!

CRYSTAL PALACE
PRESENTS
DALE DALE
THE ENTERTAINER
SCOTTY
THE VENTRILOQUIST

Incredible! You were right all along, Holmes!... Dale really was a third-rate music hall performer!

Exactly, and...

LOOK OUT, HOLMES!

Humph! It's the old story of Colonel Moran and his airgun all over again!

Yes, they've even rented a flat across the road from us like last time, do you see?...

...except they didn't use an airgun this time, though! They used a bow and arrow! What a charmingly old-fashioned way of delivering a message!

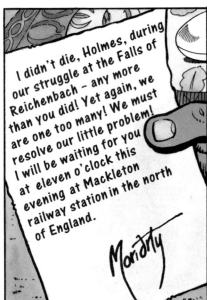

I didn't die, Holmes, during our struggle at the Falls of Reichenbach – any more than you did! Yet again, we are one too many! We must resolve our little problem! I will be waiting for you at eleven o'clock this evening at Mackleton railway station in the north of England.

Moriarty

Don't go, Holmes! It's bound to be a trap!

Moriarty is alive! The Napoleon of crime! the evil monster! It is my duty, Holmes, to accept his challenge!

But it seems he can make himself invisible!

So can I... when I'm in the mood, Holmes!

32A

That evening at Mackleton Station...

MACKLETON STATION

NEWS

SLIG SLIG

32B

I put on a brave face for Watson's sake, but if Moriarty can REALLY make himself invisible, I've got myself into a bit of a pickle...

...Like me, that evil genius is brilliant at disguises... I need to be on my guard against the people I can see as well as the people I can't see!

The place is deserted! No one around! Now does that mean Moriarty is here or not?

What's this? A train coming? But there aren't supposed to be any more trains till tomorrow!

!

Red carriage, of course!... And 'M' for Moriarty – I might have guessed!

Well, I'll be!... That door's opening... like an invitation to jump on board... Now where on earth could this ghost train be taking me...?

The invisible man, eh? I wonder now... Perhaps he's waiting for me to...

!?

He must be hiding between two carriages or underneath...

Ah! There he is!

Hands up! Ghost or no ghost, this time I'm going to blow your brains out...

Just at that moment, the train suddenly gathered speed.

!

KLANG!

BANG! BANG!

...HA HA!...

BANG

HA HA

HO! HO! HO!

Later...

And he just ran off into the night, even though I'd shot him three times!

Perhaps your hand was shaking, Holmes!

No! That's impossible! I took careful aim each time!

Hum!

You don't believe me, do you?... But wait a moment!... Who has got the train moving again? WHO?

I don't... er...

This demon seems to have power over events – or over machines, anyway! I'm...

Holmes! Carrington!

The blighter got away, Holmes!

How is Lord Reginald?

He's lost consciousness!. . . He had a terrible shock. . . Perhaps he's coming round. . .

I. . . I can hear you, Holmes!

I. . . I need to rest. . . rest. . . but if it's the last thing you do, Holmes, save me from the RED DEATH!

Trust me, Lord Reginald!

Is he safe in this room, Mr Holmes? I've closed the shutters, and there's only one door. . .

. . . and we'll lock that! What about the chimney, though?

I have an idea! We'll keep the fire burning! Not even the devil would try and get in that way!

That should do it! We've locked the door, and we're not going to let the key out of our sight! Perhaps you'd like to rest a little as well, Lady Violet. . . Carrington?

I'll stay here with you, if you don't mind!

Same here!

So nobody can get into the room, then! A detective problem for the connoisseur, eh, what? Watson?

Yes, and I'll be fascinated to see how Moriarty tries to solve it, Holmes!

Open up! IT'S ME, MYCROFT!

Mycroft! He'd only have come in an emergency! I'll go and let him in, but keep your eyes on the door, Watson, whatever else you do!

You can trust me!

What?

Yes, Watson! Lady Violet and Carrington had this fiendish plan for getting their hands on the fortunes of rich members of the aristocracy – **and starting with Lord Reginald!**

The Grand Duke and others were all brought to the 'Red Leech' – the tables were rigged, of course. Those who refused to pay up, and anyone who tried to expose them were tortured by thirsty leeches – that was doubtless the fate of poor Dale the music hall artiste turned butler!

What about Moriarty! He's kidnapped the Prime Minister! Don't you understand?

Moriarty was pulling the strings – the others were mere puppets who did as they were told! His ultimate aim was to destabilise the British Government at a critical moment! . . .

Sherlock! The Prime Minister – we've got to find him!

All in good time! You'll find he's being held by Moriarty and Moran. . . in a place guarded by the police where no one would dream of looking!. . .

. . .And that reminds me, Mycroft! Tell Inspector Lestrade to come and arrest these two crooks, will you?

Reginald! Please listen to me! It was all a terrible mistake. . . I do love you!

44A

Please forgive. . .

I wonder what you would have done if you had hated me! You were after my money, that's all! Don't worry, Holmes! They won't get away! They can wait here until Lestrade and his men get here. . .

Later. . .

44B

Why here, Holmes?

It's obvious! This place is locked and guarded! What better hiding place?

We'll have to be on our guard – don't forget Moriarty is invisible!

Ha! Ha! He's no more invisible than you or I, Watson!

Mr. Holmes!

Ah! You know who I am! Be so good as to break these seals. . . AND COME WITH ME!

45

G. CLAIRG 90.

46A

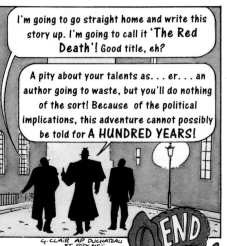